THE LITTLE OWL & THE CLOUD

WRITTEN BY **Tim Brown**

ILLUSTRATED BY Svetlana Dragicevic

FOR MY GIRLS!
AMY, IVY & OLIVE
X

ONCE UPON A TIME IN A FOREST NOT SO FAR FROM HERE
THERE GREW A MIGHTY OAK TREE, WHICH HAD STOOD FOR MANY, MANY A YEAR
INSIDE THE OLD OAK AMONGST IT'S KNOBBLY BRANCHES ENTWINED
LIVED A BEAUTIFUL LITTLE OWL, WHO WAS CURIOUS, BRAVE AND KIND

ONE CRISP MORNING AS THE LIGHT CREPT THROUGH THE LEAVES
THE LITTLE OWL LEFT HER NEST AND TOOK OFF HIGH ABOVE THE TREES
SHE SWOOOPED AND SWOONED, AND LOOPED THE LOOP LIKE ANY OTHER DAY
BUT COMPLETELY MISSED A FLUFFY CLOUD FLYING THE OTHER WAY

"LOOK OUT, LOOK OUT, YOU'RE GOING TO." SANG A LITTLE ROBIN PASSING BY.
TOO LATE. THEY HIT EACH OTHER WITH SUCH A FORCE THEY NEARLY FELL OUT OF THE SKY
BOTH A LITTLE DAZED THEY STARED NOT KNOWING WHAT TO DO
UNTIL THE CLOUD BEGAN TO LAUGH, WHICH MADE THE LITTLE OWL LAUGH TOO.

"I'M SO SORRY ARE YOU OK, I DIDN'T SEE YOU THROUGH THE GLARE"
"YES I'M FINE, MY HEADS A LITTLE FLUFFY BUT THERE'S NOTHING UNUSUAL THERE"
THEY BURST OUT LAUGHING ONCE AGAIN AND COULDN'T STOP, TRY AS THEY MAY
ONLY WHEN THEY COULD LAUGH NO MORE THE LITTLE OWL ASKED "WOULD YOU LIKE TO PLAY?"

THEY RACED AND DANCED, PLAYED HIDE AND SEEK AND TAG, SIMON SAYS, I SPY
MORE HIDE AND SEEK, A BIT MORE TAG, THEN PIGGY IN MIDDLE WITH A PASSING MAGPIE
AND WHEN THEY BOTH EVENTUALLY GREW TIRED, AND FINISHED THEIR LAST RACE
THE LITTLE OWL LAID HER HEAD DOWN IN THE CLOUDS SOFT, WARM EMBRACE

AS MORNING PASSED THE SKY TURNED GREY SLOWLY SHUTTING OUT THE SUN
WHICH THE LITTLE OWL AND THE CLOUD HAD MISSED WHILST HAVING SO MUCH FUN
SUDDENLY A DROP OF RAIN FELL ONTO THE OWLS BEAK
SHE LOOKED AROUND TO SEE A TEAR FALLING DOWN HER FRIENDS SOFT CHEEK

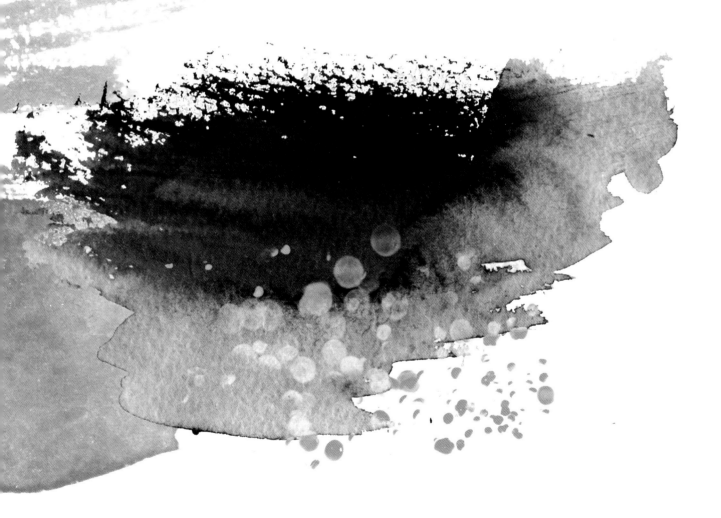

ONE TEAR FOLLOWED ANOTHER, AND ANOTHER UNTIL IT BEGAN TO POUR
AS IT POURED THE CLOUD GOT SMALLER, UNTIL EVENTUALLY HE WAS NO MORE
THE LITTLE OWL FEELING LOST AND SCARED SET OFF TO LOOK FOR HER NEW FRIEND
FIRST TO THE LAKE, THEN THE GLADE, THEN FOLLOWED THE RIVER TO THE FOREST'S END

"CLOUD WHERE ARE YOU? WHERE ARE YOU CLOUD?" DESPERATE FOR A REPLY
SHE SEARCHED AND SEARCHED AND SEARCHED UNTIL SHE COULD NO LONGER FLY
TIRED AND THIRSTY SHE FLUTTERED TO THE GROUND TO REST HER WEARY WINGS
LANDING NEXT TO A FRESH ROUND PUDDLE OF ALL THE MANY POSSIBLE THINGS

SHE LENT OVER TO TAKE A DRINK AND WAS SHOCKED AT WHAT SHE SAW
FOR THERE SMILING BACK AT HER WAS THE FRIEND SHE'D BEEN LOOKING FOR
NO LONGER WHITE AND FLUFFY BUT STILL HER FRIEND NONE THE LESS
"IT'S ME, IT'S ME" THE PUDDLE REPLIED, "I KNOW, I KNOW, I LOOK A MESS".

THE LITTLE OWL AND THE CLOUD - NOW PUDDLE, WERE AS HAPPY AS COULD BE
THEY COULDN'T SHARE A FLUFFY HUG, OR SHOOT ACROSS THE SKY CAREFREE
BUT FINALLY THEY HAD FOUND EACH OTHER AND THAT IS ALL THEY CARED
THE LITTLE OWL ASKED THE CLOUD, "WHERE DID YOU GO, I'VE BEEN SO SCARED?"

HE PAUSED, "I WILL NOT BE A CLOUD FOREVER BUT I WILL NEVER DISAPPEAR"
"LOOK AROUND, AND YOU WILL FIND ME IN A PUDDLE, STREAM, OR EVEN IN A TEAR"
AS SURE AS SEASONS COME ROUND EACH YEAR THEY NEVER REALLY END
SO EVEN WHEN I'M NOT AROUND I WILL ALWAYS BE YOUR FRIEND

AS THEY TALKED AND LAUGHED THE CLOUDS ABOVE OPENED LIKE A DOOR
LETTING IN THE SUN'S WARM RAYS WHICH BEGAN TO DRY THE FOREST FLOOR
AND JUST LIKE THAT THE PUDDLE DISAPPEARED UP INTO THE SKY
BUT, THE LITTLE OWL WASN'T TOO SAD, AS SHE KNEW THIS WASN'T GOODBYE.